CW00394005

PLAYALONG FLUTE CHRISTMAS HITS

Published by
WISE PUBLICATIONS
14-15 Berners Street, London W1T 3LJ,
United Kingdom.

Exclusive Distributors:
MUSIC SALES LIMITED
Distribution Centre, Newmarket Road, Bury St Edmunds, Suffolk IP33 3YB,
United Kingdom.
MUSIC SALES PTY LIMITED
Units 3-4, 17 Willfox Street, Condell Park, NSW 2200, Australia.

Order No. AM1007204
ISBN 978-1-78305-239-4
This book © Copyright 2013 Wise Publications, a division of Music Sales Limited.

Compiled and edited by Jenni Norey.
Cover designed by Michael Bell Design.
Printed in the EU.

Your Guarantee of Quality:
As publishers, we strive to produce every book to the highest commercial standards.
This book has been carefully designed to minimise awkward page turns and
to make playing from it a real pleasure.
Particular care has been given to specifying acid-free, neutral-sized paper made from
pulps which have not been elemental chlorine bleached.
This pulp is from farmed sustainable forests and was produced with special regard for the environment.
Throughout, the printing and binding have been planned to ensure a sturdy,
attractive publication which should give years of enjoyment.
If your copy fails to meet our high standards, please inform us and we will gladly replace it.

www.musicsales.com

31 MELODY LINE ARRANGEMENTS +
31 mp3 BACKING TRACKS +
31 mp3 DEMO TRACKS!

PLAYALONG FLUTE CHRISTMAS HITS

WISE PUBLICATIONS
part of The Music Sales Group
London / New York / Paris / Sydney / Copenhagen / Berlin / Madrid / Hong Kong / Tokyo

SEE PAGE 80 FOR DETAILS OF HOW TO ACCESS YOUR TRACKS

A Spaceman Came Travelling

Words & Music by Chris de Burgh

All I Want For Christmas Is You

Words & Music by Mariah Carey & Walter Afanasieff

Baby, It's Cold Outside

Words & Music by Frank Loesser

Blue Christmas

Words & Music by Billy Hayes & Jay Johnson

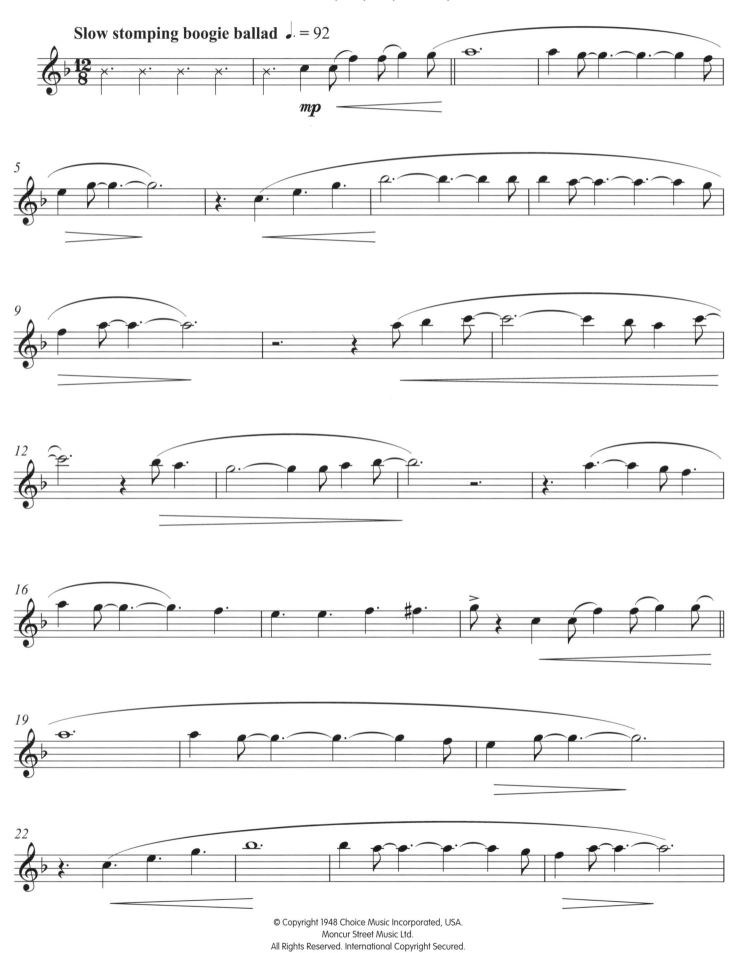

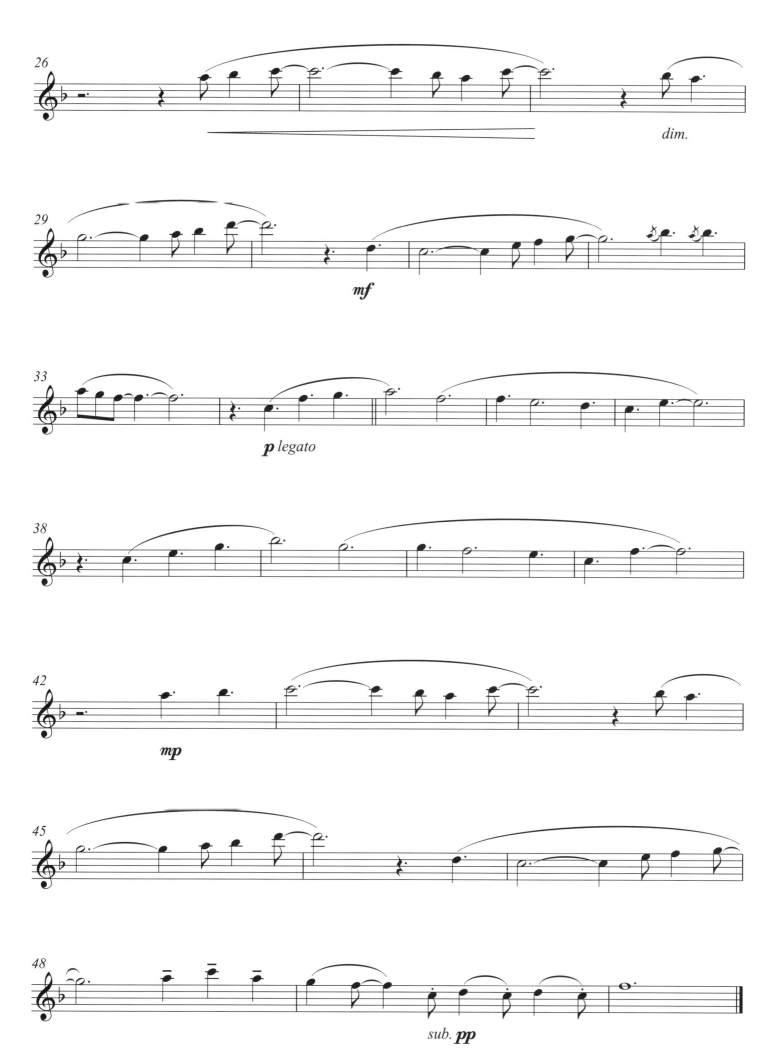

C-H-R-I-S-T-M-A-S

Words by Jenny Lou Carson
Music by Eddy Arnold

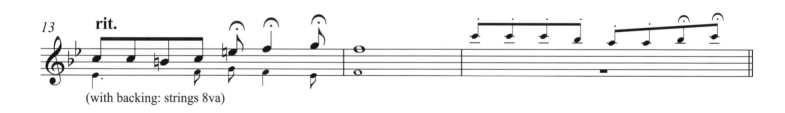

(with backing: strings 16va)

The Christmas Song
(Chestnuts Roasting On An Open Fire)

Words & Music by Mel Torme & Robert Wells

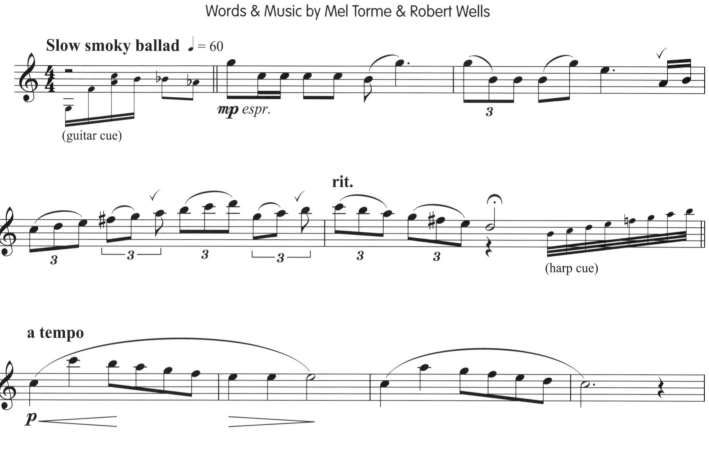

The Christmas Waltz

Words by Sammy Cahn
Music by Jule Styne

Fairytale Of New York

Words & Music by Shane MacGowan & Jem Finer

Happy Xmas (War Is Over)

Words & Music by John Lennon & Yoko Ono

Hark! The Herald Angels Sing

Words by Charles Wesley
Music by Felix Mendelssohn

Broadly (♩ = 92)

Have Yourself A Merry Little Christmas

Words & Music by Hugh Martin & Ralph Blane

Steadily and smoothly ♩ = 88

mp espressivo

to Coda ⊕

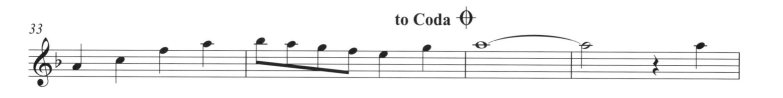

D.S. al Coda   ⊕ **Coda**   **Slower**

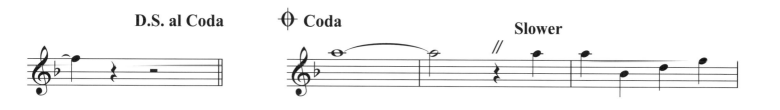

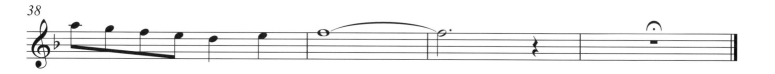

(There's No Place Like) Home For The Holidays

Words & Music by Al Stillman & Robert Allen

Showtime singalong feel, swung ♪s (♩ = 158)

f *jolly, non legato*

mf

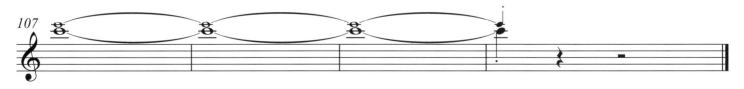

Here Comes Santa Claus
(Right Down Santa Claus Lane)

Words & Music by Gene Autry & Oakley Haldeman

I Believe In Father Christmas

Words & Music by Greg Lake & Peter Sinfield

I Saw Mommy Kissing Santa Claus

Words & Music by Tommie Connor

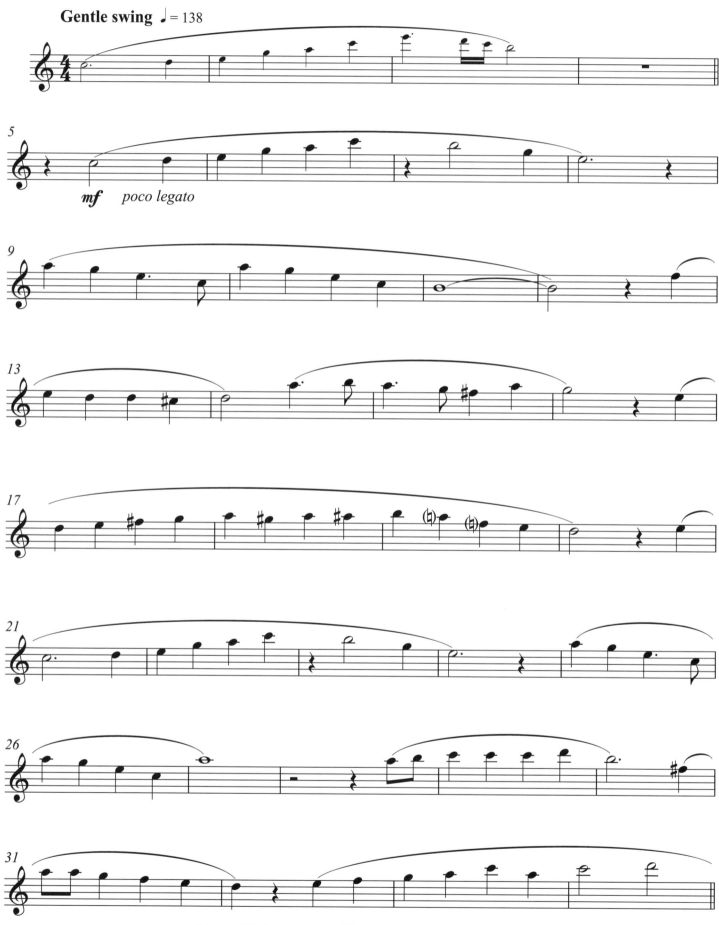

mf legato again

p

sub. f

In Dulci Jubilo

Words & Music Traditional

Brightly, with a bounce ♩. = 120

mf ritmico

(guitar solo)

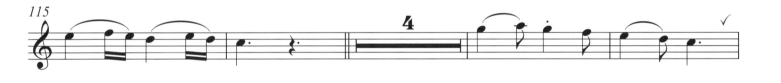

molto rit.

I Wish It Could Be Christmas Every Day

Words & Music by Roy Wood

Jingle Bells

Words & Music by James Lord Pierpont

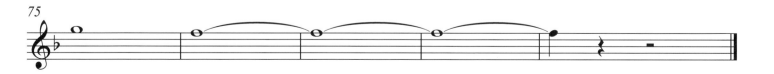

Jingle Bell Rock

Words & Music by Joseph Beal & James Boothe

Merry Xmas Everybody

Words & Music by Neville Holder & James Lea

poco rall.

Let It Snow! Let It Snow! Let It Snow!

Words by Sammy Cahn
Music by Jule Styne

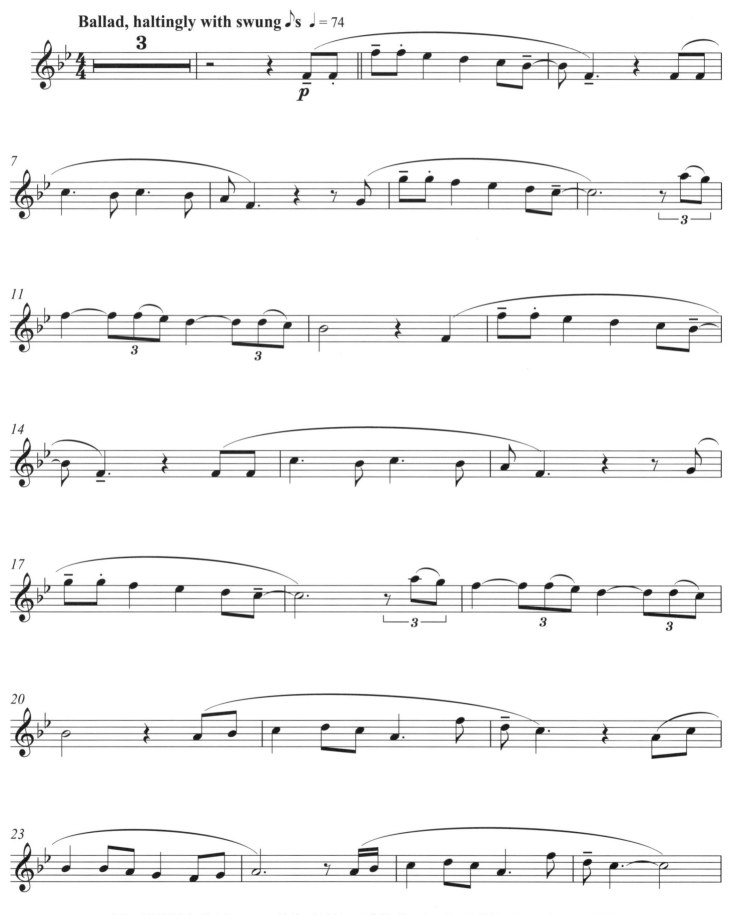

Lonely This Christmas

Words & Music by Nicky Chinn & Mike Chapman

Mistletoe And Wine

Words by Leslie Stewart & Jeremy Paul
Music by Keith Strachan

poco rall.   A tempo

f

rall.

Wonderful Christmastime

Words & Music by Paul McCartney

dim.

Peace On Earth/Little Drummer Boy

Words by Alan Kohan
Music by Larry Grossman & Ian Fraser

In a stately manner ♩ = 72

mp dolce

mf espressivo

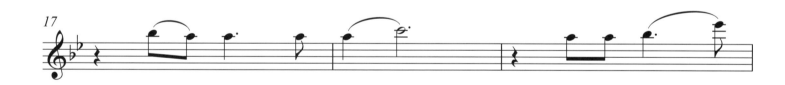

mp

Santa Baby

Words & Music by Joan Javits, Phil Springer & Tony Springer

Sleigh Ride

Words by Mitchell Parish
Music by Leroy Anderson

D.S. al Coda

Coda

molto rall.

Silent Night

Words by Joseph Mohr
Music by Franz Gruber

Peacefully ♩ = 76
(piano cue)

to Coda ⊕

A tempo, espressivo

poco rit.   **A tempo**   **D.S. al Coda**

Coda   poco rall.

A tempo, slower

Stop The Cavalry

Words & Music by Jona Lewie

Walking In The Air
(Theme from 'The Snowman')

Words & Music by Howard Blake

Winter Wonderland

Words by Richard Smith
Music by Felix Bernard

123456789

HOW TO DOWNLOAD YOUR MUSIC TRACKS

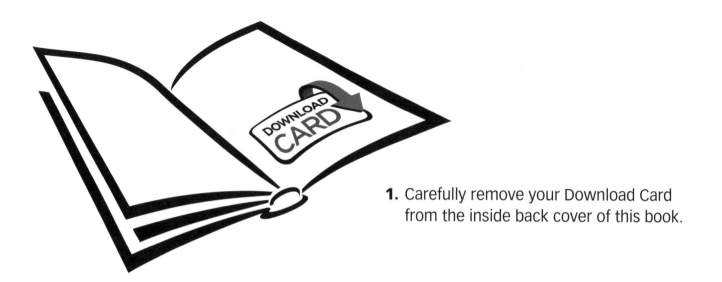

1. Carefully remove your Download Card from the inside back cover of this book.

2. On the back of the card is your unique access code. Enter this at www.musicsalesdownloads.com

TO REDEEM THIS CARD VISIT
www.musicsalesdownloads.com

ENTER ACCESS CODE:

XXXXXXXXX

Download Cards are powered by Dropcards.
User must accept terms at dropcards.com/terms
which are adopted by The Music Sales Group.
Not reedemable for cash. Void where prohibited or restricted by law.

DCARD1006478

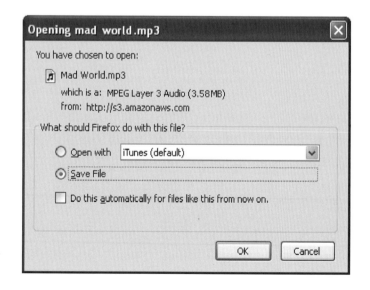

3. Follow the instructions to save your files to your computer*. That's it!

*Appearance of download manager will vary depending upon operating system and web browser.
In case of difficulty when downloading files, please contact dropcards.com/help
Card missing? Please contact music@musicsales.co.uk